The Caves of LASCAUX

written by Diane Hoyt-Goldsmith

illustrated by Sanford Kossin

McGraw-Hill
School Division

New York   Farmington

The Discovery

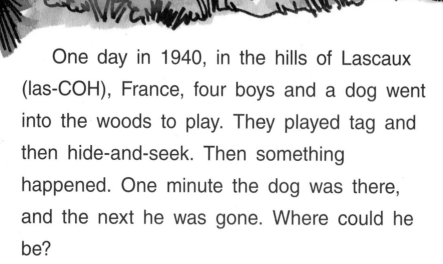

One day in 1940, in the hills of Lascaux
(las-COH), France, four boys and a dog went
into the woods to play. They played tag and
then hide-and-seek. Then something
happened. One minute the dog was there,
and the next he was gone. Where could he
be?

The boys stopped playing. This was
serious. They started to look for the dog.
They called his name again and again. Only
the wind in the trees answered.

"Look!" said one boy. "There's a hole here."

Another boy had an idea.

"Maybe Robot fell into it," he said.

He pulled at the rocks to make the hole larger. Then they all began to dig.

Soon the hole was big enough for a boy
to go through. One by one, they went down
into the dark.

Down, down, down they went, deep
into the earth.

"We have found a cave!" one boy cried.

"It's big," said another.

"And it's very dark," said a small voice.

They called the dog again. Still there was
no answer.

"We'll have to go home and get some
lights," one of the boys decided. "Robot will
be all right for a while."

The next day, the boys made their way
back to the cave. This time they had a lamp.
They called the dog again. Then they
heard the sound of running feet. The dog
came back! He was happy to see the boys.

They began to look around. The cave had
many rooms. Some of them were very large.
Then they found a room with beautiful
paintings on the walls.

The boys wanted to find out more about
the paintings. Who had made them? And
why? They decided to tell their teacher, Mr.
Léon Laval, about their discovery.

Sharing the News

Mr. Laval smiled when he saw the four boys and their dog coming into his garden. The boys told their teacher all about the dog going down the hole and about finding the cave. They all started to talk at once.

"Remember," Mr. Laval said laughing, "I can only listen to one of you at a time!"

When Mr. Laval heard about the
beautiful paintings of animals, he became
serious. He told the boys, "This cave you
have found is very special. I believe it may
be an important discovery."

Mr. Laval told the boys that he would like to send a message to a man he knew in Paris.

"This man knows a lot about caves," he told them. "He may know about the people who made the paintings, too.

"He is a priest," Mr. Laval continued, "and he is also a famous teacher. He learns about the past by looking at the things people have left behind."

After a few days, the priest arrived from Paris. The boys took Father Henri Breuil to the cave.

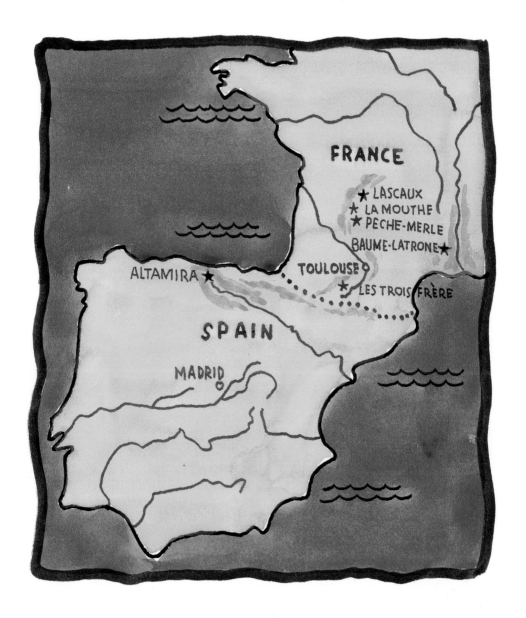

There are many painted caves in Europe.
Many of these, like the caves at Lascaux,
were discovered by children.

Life in the Ice Age

They stopped to look at the paintings in one of the largest rooms. Father Henri began to tell them about the people who made the pictures on the walls.

"These paintings were made by people during the Ice Age. That was more than 10,000 years ago," he said.

"That's even older than my grandmother," one boy said.

"Yes," the priest laughed. "Quite a lot older."

The priest told the boys what the world was like during the Ice Age. He said the land where they stood was once covered by ice and snow.

People who lived in those days hunted many kinds of animals. They used the meat for food. They made warm clothing out of the skins. Sometimes people lived inside the caves to keep warm.

Father Henri told the boys that the paintings in the cave at Lascaux were among the most beautiful he had ever seen. He said that they would help people learn about what life was like during the Ice Age.

"You boys have made an important discovery," he said with a smile.

And to think it all happened because four boys and a dog went out to play one day in the hills of Lascaux.